At CGP, we have a fiction addiction...

...and that's why we've made this SAT Buster Fiction Reading Book 2!
It's bursting with more fantastic practice at the same level as Book 1 — and
it covers all eight reading elements that are tested in the KS2 English SATs:

2a Word Meanings   **2e** Predictions

2b Fact Retrieval   **2f** Structure

2c Summarising   **2g** Language

2d Inferences   **2h** Comparisons

There are separate question pages for each element, so it's simple
for pupils to spot what they're being asked to do. What's more, the fun
Tellastaurius tick-boxes make it easy to keep track of their progress.

And if they've breezed through everything in Books 1 and 2, try out our
SAT Buster Stretch Reading books to give them more of a challenge!

Published by CGP

Editors: Marc Barnard, Emma Bonney, Izzy Bowen,
Andy Cashmore, Sophie Herring, Catherine Heygate,
Gabrielle Richardson and James Summersgill.

With thanks to Emma Crighton and Juliette Green
for the proofreading.

With thanks to Jan Greenway for the copyright
research.

ISBN: 978 1 78908 094 0

Clipart from Corel®
Printed by Elanders Ltd, Newcastle upon Tyne.

Based on the classic CGP style created by Richard Parsons.

Text, design, layout and original illustrations
© Coordination Group Publications Ltd. (CGP) 2018
All rights reserved.

Fact Retrieval Questions

For FACT RETRIEVAL questions, you need to read the text closely and pick out the information that you need for the answers. Have another nosey around the text, then have a go at these.

1. Read the paragraph that begins **'Then, even worse than all that...'**

   Write down **one** thing Connor's dad told Connor to do on school photo day.

   ....

   1 mark

2. Read the paragraph that begins **'Connor thought this was unreasonable...'**

   According to Connor, why did Ellie start crying?

   Tick **one** box.

   She didn't want to sit still for the photo. ☐

   She didn't like the carrots in her lunch. ☐

   She didn't like sitting next to Connor. ☐

   She didn't want to wait her turn. ☐

   1 mark

3. Where was last year's school photo hung up?

   ....

   1 mark

4. Look at page 4.

   Use the information from the text to match up the actions with who was doing them. The first one has been done for you.

   Connor's dad   **running around the garden**

   Ellie   **playing with toys**

   Pepper   **making breakfast**

   1 mark

Keep turning... ➡

The Perfect Photo

School photo day made Connor's stomach churn. The process was unpleasant from start to finish. You had to wait for ages for your turn. You had to sit still and not fidget. You had to smile sweetly while the camera stared threateningly at you.

Then, even worse than all that, was Connor's dad. His dad took school photo day very seriously. "Make sure you smile properly. Sit up straight. Keep your jumper clean. And avoid making your little sister cry like last year."

Connor thought this was unreasonable. He hadn't made Ellie cry. She had started crying because she didn't like the carrots in her lunch. It had ruined the photo. The picture had been hung up in the living room for a whole year as an unfortunate reminder of the day.

But none of that was going to happen this time. Ellie wasn't going to cry. Connor would resist pulling a silly face. His dad would have a nice photo to put in a frame and give to Connor's grandma on her birthday. Everything would be as it was supposed to be.

Except Connor couldn't find his school jumper.

A bundle of nerves, Connor checked the wardrobe and found nothing. Then he ransacked the large pile of dirty clothes on the floor next to his bed. Still nothing. Refusing to give up — he knew it must be somewhere — he upended the laundry basket and then ran downstairs to look in the washing machine. Nothing.

"Connor!" his dad's voice boomed from somewhere in the house. "Come to the kitchen — I'm making breakfast!"

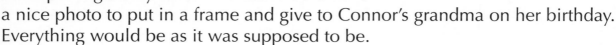

Connor hesitated. He could hear his sister giggling as she played with her toys, and Pepper the dog running about in the garden. Connor imagined turning up to his photo without his jumper, thinking of how much his dad cared about the picture, and gulped.

"It has to be here somewhere," he muttered to himself, still sure that he would find his jumper. "Think, Connor." He had only been wearing it yesterday. How had he managed to lose it since then?

Connor headed back up to his room, lay himself down on the cluttered carpet and peered under his bed. There was a grimy pair of socks, a few discarded wrappers and a trainer that had been the loser in a savage battle with Pepper. But there was no school jumper. He was running out of time.

"Connor!" his dad called again. His voice had a more severe tone this time.

"Coming!" Connor called back. He sighed, deciding to stop searching for his jumper, thinking he'd never find it. As he grabbed his schoolbag from the bed, his red school jumper tumbled out. "Aha!" he shouted, picking it up and holding it aloft like a trophy. He wrenched it over his head and sprinted back down the stairs.

In the kitchen, Connor's dad was buttering slices of toast. The dog was still in the garden, making light work of the flowerbeds. "Pepper!" his dad opened the window and shouted at her from the kitchen. "Leave the flowers alone!"

Pepper ignored him. "Connor, can you bring her back inside?"

Holding a slice of toast in one hand, Connor went into the next room and pulled the back door open. Pepper looked up at the sound. She barked excitedly and bounded towards him.

"Oh no," Connor said, realising what was about to happen. He dropped the toast and thrust his hands out in front of him.

But it was too late. Pepper sped through the door and leapt up to greet him. Soil flew everywhere. Connor was spattered with dirt and mud and even a few flower petals. There were two brown paw prints right on the front of his jumper.

At the noise, Connor's dad poked his head out of the kitchen. Connor turned to him in horror. His dad looked at Connor with wide eyes. Then he pulled his phone out of his pocket and took a picture. "Best school photo yet," he said, laughing.

The Perfect Photo

This story is about the morning of a school photo day. Connor's dad really wants his son to bring home a nice photo. However, when Connor is getting ready for school, things don't go quite as planned...

What to do —

1) Open out the folding pages, and read the story *The Perfect Photo*.

2) Then, wiggle your whole body from head to toe, as quickly as you can.

3) Once you're feeling limbered up, have one more read of the text, then move on to the questions.

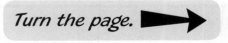

Turn the page.

Fact Retrieval Questions

5. Read the paragraph beginning '**'It has to be here somewhere...**'

When did Connor last wear his jumper?

....

| 1 mark |

6. Give **two** places Connor searched for his jumper.

....

....

| 2 marks |

7. What colour is Connor's school jumper?

| blue | yellow | green | red |

| 1 mark |

Circle your answer.

8. Why did Connor open the door to the garden?

| to water the flowers | to play with Pepper | to bring Pepper inside | to pose for a photo |

| 1 mark |

Circle your answer.

9. Look at the last paragraph.

Why did Connor's dad look out of the kitchen?

....

....

| 1 mark |

Tellastauriuses have huge nostrils, which they use to sniff out facts. How did you find these pages?

Section 1 — The Perfect Photo

2d

Inference Questions

INFERENCE questions are all about looking beyond what's most obvious in the text and thinking a bit more deeply about it. See how you get on with these questions.

1. In the first paragraph, Connor feels

| worried | | excited | | hungry | | patient |

1 mark

Circle your answer.

2. Read the paragraph beginning **'A bundle of nerves...'**

How can you tell that Connor was determined to find his jumper?

Give **one** way.

....

1 mark

3. Read the paragraph beginning **'Connor hesitated...'**

How did Connor think his dad would react if he wasn't wearing his school jumper for the photo?

....

1 mark

4. Read the paragraph beginning **'Connor headed back up to his room...'**

What evidence is there in this paragraph that Connor is messy?

Give **two** things.

....

....

2 marks

5. Find and copy a sentence from page 5 which tells you Connor's dad was getting frustrated that Connor hadn't come downstairs.

....

1 mark

Inference Questions

2d

6. Read the paragraph beginning '**"Coming!" Connor called back...**'

How do you think Connor felt when he found his school jumper?

Use evidence from the text to support your answer.

....

....

| 2 marks |

7. Look at page 5.

Find and copy a sentence that suggests Pepper was happy to see Connor.

....

....

| 1 mark |

8. '**He dropped the toast and thrust his hands out in front of him.**'

Why did Connor put his hands out in front of him?

| 1 mark |

....

9. a) At what time of day does the story take place?

| morning | midday | afternoon | evening |

| 1 mark |

Circle your answer.

b) How can you tell? Give **one** way.

| 1 mark |

....

Tellastauriuses can answer inference questions while stampeding through the jungle. Can you?

Section 1 — The Perfect Photo

Word Meaning Questions

WORD MEANING questions are a chance to show off your vocabulary skills. They're all about whether you've understood the words in the text. Read the text again and then try these ones.

1. Read the first paragraph.

   Which word in this paragraph could be replaced by the word 'nicely'?

   ....

   1 mark

2. '...he upended the laundry basket and then ran downstairs...'

   What does the word **'upended'** mean in this sentence?

pushed		picked up		turned over		dropped

   Circle your answer.

   1 mark

3. Read the paragraph beginning '**'It has to be here somewhere...'**

   Which word in this paragraph tells you that Connor was speaking quietly?

   ....

   1 mark

4. '**She barked excitedly and bounded towards him.**'

   Which of the words below is closest to the meaning of **'bounded'** in this sentence?

   Tick **one** box.

   marched ☐

   crept ☐

   turned ☐

   ran ☐

   1 mark

Tellastauriuses love reading dictionaries to learn new words. They also love eating them. How did you do?

2c ## Summary Questions

For SUMMARY questions, you need to think about the overall meaning of the whole text or of big chunks of it. Have a go at answering these two superb summary questions below.

1. Read from **'A bundle of nerves...'** to **'...running out of time.'**

Which sentence best summarises these paragraphs?

| Pepper destroys a trainer. | Connor finds his school jumper. | Connor searches the house. | Connor cleans his room. |

1 mark

Circle your answer.

2. Tick the option which is a main idea of the text.

Connor gets nervous easily. ☐

Ellie cries all the time. ☐

School photos are fun. ☐

Connor doesn't want to upset his dad. ☐

1 mark

2f ## Structure Question

STRUCTURE questions are all about when things happen in the text and when things change. Have one last read through the text, thinking about this, then try your hand at this question.

1. At first, Connor was hopeful about finding his jumper.

Find and copy the sentence where Connor's feelings about finding his jumper changed.

....

1 mark

....

Tellastauriuses take to summary and structure questions like ducks to water. How did you find them?

Fact Retrieval Questions

The next two pages are all about FACT RETRIEVAL, which means finding bits of information in the text. Read each question carefully, and then look for the answers in 'Chioke's Chance'.

1. Read the first paragraph on page 13.

    Give **one** thing that Chioke had been remembering from last year's carnival.

    ....   **1 mark**

2. When he went downstairs, Chioke made a birthday wish.

    Why had Chioke never told anyone his wish?

    Tick **one** box.

    He liked to keep secrets. ☐

    His sister said it wouldn't come true if he did. ☐

    His sister would make fun of him. ☐

    He forgot about it. ☐   **1 mark**

3. When did Chioke start learning to dance? Circle your answer.

    | one year ago | two years ago | three years ago | four years ago |

    1 mark

4. Look at the last paragraph on page 13.

    What does Chioke enjoy about dancing?

    ....   **1 mark**

5. Read the paragraph beginning **'When Chioke discovered the dance troupe...'**

    Give **two** things Chioke likes about Jewel.

    ....

    ....   **2 marks**

Chioke's Chance

The day had finally arrived. For weeks, Chioke's mind had been buzzing with memories of the bright lights, the multi-coloured signs and the loud music of last year's carnival — and now he was going to get to go again as a special birthday treat. He couldn't wait to find out who this year's mystery guest performer would be.

Chioke leapt out of bed and raced downstairs. He skidded to a halt when he saw at least twenty people gathered in the kitchen around an enormous cake.

"Happy Birthday, Chioke!" chorused his family, bursting out laughing at the look on his face.

"You didn't think any of us would have missed your birthday did you, my dear?" asked his grandma, gently ruffling his hair.

"Blow out your candles, Chioke," encouraged his mum, "and don't forget your wish!"

He'd made the same wish on his last two birthdays, and although it hadn't come true yet, he was still optimistic. His older sister Kalisha had sternly informed him that revealing his wish would stop it coming true, and so he had never breathed a word of it to anyone.

Chioke had started to dance in secret four years ago. He was sure his dad wouldn't approve, so he only practised when his dad was watching the football. He wasn't very good at first, always stumbling over his own feet. He loved the way the music made him feel, though, and so, despite the odd dance disaster, he kept going.

The story continues over the page. ➡

When Chioke discovered the dance troupe Jewel, he was mesmerised by their talent and enthusiasm. He loved their dance style, which was like nothing he'd ever seen before, and was determined to master it. He spent hours on end analysing their videos online and carefully repeating move after move until he knew every routine by heart. He'd only told Kalisha about his passion — Chioke didn't even mention it to his friends, and he thought it best to keep it that way, worrying about the jokes they'd make.

His birthday was a blur of cake and presents, but the best was yet to come. That night, the carnival was spectacular, and before Chioke knew it, it was almost time for the mystery guest appearance.

Suddenly, he saw his dad rushing over.

"Chioke, follow me!" Then he was off again before Chioke could utter a word. Chioke was annoyed that his dad was being so mysterious and that they might miss the show, but he felt he had no choice but to go with him.

Chioke found himself being guided into a small tent, and then he was face to face with none other than Josh Gatesley, the lead dancer of Jewel.

Chioke stared at Josh and then his father, completely speechless. Luckily, his dad took over, his words spilling over each other. "I overheard the group saying that they might not be able to perform tonight because Will was injured in rehearsals, and it gave me an idea. I suggested that you might be able to dance with them, and Josh here agreed to give you a chance."

When Chioke said nothing, he added, "Mum and I know how much you practise — you're not as good at hiding it as you think, son. What do you say?"

Chioke was still lost for words, but there was no time for discussion. Josh pressed play on a CD player, and music filled the tent. Without thinking, Chioke began to follow the steps he had practised a thousand times.

No more than thirty seconds later, Josh stopped the CD. Chioke's heart sank.

But Josh's face widened into an enthusiastic grin. "That was fantastic! You can really move, Chioke! Please will you help us?"

The next fifteen minutes passed quickly as the group led Chioke through their final preparations. With two minutes to go, the dancers silently shrugged into their famous leather jackets, which had the troupe name in huge, gold, glittery letters on the back. Josh glanced over at Chioke and nodded towards the one remaining jacket. "That one's for you, kiddo."

Stepping out onto the stage, Chioke was temporarily blinded by the spotlights and deafened by the cheers from the crowd. Then, as his eyes got used to the lights, he caught sight of his parents in the front row, both waving, their eyes glistening.

The music started almost immediately, and the time for nerves had passed. Song after song blasted from the speakers and the dancers moved in perfect harmony. They performed a series of complex moves, all perfectly in time with the music. The crowd cheered and applauded throughout. Chioke twirled and jumped and leapt, as if he had always been part of the troupe. He didn't put a foot wrong, and when the show ended, the Jewel dancers hoisted him off stage on their shoulders, chanting his name.

Later that night, Chioke collapsed into bed with the roars of the crowd still ringing in his ears, amazed by his incredible achievement. He thought of his friends and knew they would have been impressed. He would be forever grateful to Kalisha for never letting him give away his birthday wish.

Chioke's Chance

What do you wish for when you blow out the candles on your birthday cake?
Don't tell anyone or it might not come true! 'Chioke's Chance' is a story
about a boy who is very careful to keep his birthday wish a secret...

What to do —

1) Open out the folding pages, and
   read the story *Chioke's Chance*.

2) Then read it again to make sure you've
   got the hang of any tricky bits.

3) Now try to imagine your dream birthday
   cake. Mine's a chocolate sponge with
   tomato icing. Cake constructed, move
   on and have a go at the questions.

Turn the page. ➡

2b ## *Fact Retrieval Questions*

6. What did Chioke do to learn Jewel's dance routines? Give **two** things.

....

....

2 marks

7. Who arranged for Chioke to meet Jewel?

his mum	Kalisha	his dad	his grandma

1 mark

Circle your answer.

8. Why did Jewel need Chioke's help?

....

....

1 mark

9. Put a tick in the correct box to show whether each statement is true or false.

	True	False
Chioke had never been to the carnival before.		
Chioke practised dancing when his dad watched football.		
Chioke's parents knew he was learning to dance.		
Jewel's jackets were decorated with silver letters.		

1 mark

Tellastauriuses can answer fact retrieval questions while dancing the conga. How did you find this page?

Inference Questions

Don't worry if INFERENCE questions seem tricky at first — with a bit of practice you'll be an inference expert in no time. Have another read of the text, then tackle these questions.

1. Read the first paragraph on page 13.

How can you tell that Chioke was excited about going to the carnival?

Give **one** way.

....

1 mark

2. Read the paragraph beginning **'When Chioke discovered...'**

Find and copy a phrase that tells you Jewel's dance style was unusual.

....

1 mark

3. **'That night, the carnival was spectacular...'**

Is this a fact or an opinion?

....

1 mark

4. Read from **'Chioke stared at Josh...'** to **'...practised a thousand times.'**

How do you think Chioke felt in these paragraphs?

| disappointed | upset | irritated | astonished |

Circle your answer.

1 mark

5. Why do you think Chioke's **'heart sank'** when Josh turned the music off?

....

....

1 mark

2d	*Inference Questions*

6. '...he caught sight of his parents in the front row, both waving, their eyes glistening.'

How does this suggest Chioke's parents felt seeing him on stage?

Tick **one** box.

They didn't want him to dance. ☐

They were proud of him. ☐

They didn't care about him dancing. ☐

They were angry with him. ☐

1 mark

7. Read the paragraph beginning '**The music started almost immediately...**'

How does this paragraph make the group's performance seem impressive?

....

....

....

2 marks

8. How do you think the Jewel dancers felt about Chioke's performance?

Explain your answer using evidence from the text.

....

....

....

2 marks

Tellastauriuses think inference questions are even tastier than cheese on toast. How did you get on?

Word Meaning Questions

Words are the basic building blocks of a text, so it's pretty important to understand what they mean. Put your WORD MEANING skills to the test by answering these questions.

1. **'...although it hadn't come true yet, he was still optimistic.'**

   Which of the words below is closest in meaning to **'optimistic'**? Tick **one** box.

   calm ☐   serious ☐

   hopeful ☐   doubtful ☐

   1 mark

2. **'...always stumbling over his own feet.'**

   Circle the word which means the same as **'stumbling'** in this sentence.

   | kicking | running | jumping | tripping |

   1 mark

3. **'He spent hours on end analysing their videos online...'**

   Circle the word that could replace the word **'analysing'** in this sentence.

   | making | deleting | studying | recording |

   1 mark

4. Look at page 15.

   Find and copy a word that means 'clapped'.

   ....

   1 mark

Tellastauriuses could answer word meaning questions all day. Give yourself a tick to show how you got on.

*The last few questions on **Chioke's Chance** are under here.* ➤

Section 2 — Chioke's Chance   *© CGP — not to be photocopied*

Beneath the Waves

Leah groaned, clutching her stomach as the world jolted and swung sharply beneath her feet. The ground wasn't supposed to shift and roll like a fairground ride. She'd never realised how brilliant that was, the way the land was firm, flat and reliable and didn't make you want to throw up just by standing on it. It was hard to believe that, only this morning, she had been excited to step onto a boat for the first time. Now, an hour and a half into the eight-hour ferry journey, she had definitely changed her mind. Any excitement she had felt had shrivelled up with the first wave of nausea. She would never, ever take dry land for granted again.

She wanted to hide in the cabin with a blanket over her head and pretend that none of this was happening. Her nan had other ideas and shepherded her back up on deck. "Fresh air is what you need," she said breezily, ignoring Leah's protests. "You'll be right as rain in a few minutes."

As ever, Leah's nan had been right. Sitting on the deck of the ferry, with the cool breeze on her face and the sharp smell of salt in the air, she did feel slightly better. The sky was clear and blue, the sun's glow providing warmth against the rush of the sea air as they sped through the water. Maybe boats weren't so bad after all. She wouldn't ever make a world-class sailor, but she'd probably survive the journey. Probably.

Nearby, Leah's nan was settling into her chair delightedly. She had made herself at home with a glass of orange juice, a blueberry muffin and a shabby paperback book spread out on the table beside her. She had enthusiastically embraced being on holiday — the fact that they hadn't actually arrived yet was of little consequence — and was wearing a floppy, wide-brimmed hat, clutching it firmly to her head as it threatened to blow away into the sea.

The story continues over the page.

Section 3 — Beneath the Waves

Leah was less prepared. She hadn't brought a book or a game or even her phone up on deck with her, which she now realised was an oversight. Returning to the cabin seemed perilous right now, just when she was starting to feel better, but there was nothing else for it. She stood up and took a couple of steps forward. A sudden lurch of the boat sent her flying forwards, grappling for the handrail in a clumsy but somehow successful attempt to stay upright. Hopefully no one had noticed.

She was about to admit defeat and go back to her chair when something caught her eye. She stared intently over the handrail into the sea. It had only been for a split second, but she was sure she had seen something in the water. Had she imagined it? She was just about to turn away when she saw it again. A hand burst out of the water, followed by an arm. A person in the water alongside the boat. She opened her mouth to shout "Man overboard!", which she'd seen people do on TV when someone fell out of a boat. Then the words died in her throat.

The arm was green.

She blinked, rubbed her eyes and looked again. It was definitely green, covered in scales that glistened in the water, reflecting the sunlight. The shoulder was green, and the neck, and the head on top of it. Through the scales, two penetrating yellow eyes glinted, and long, tangled hair trailed behind the head like seaweed. She was sure the creature had met her gaze for a moment before it disappeared again under the water.

Leah clutched the handrail tightly. She stared into the water, searching for anything that would tell her that what she had seen was true. She looked for another flash of emerald scales, or a shadow beneath the surface of the water. But the boat was moving too quickly, churning the water as it ploughed through the waves. She shook her head, ashamed of her foolishness. Unless...

The head emerged from the water for a second time. Leah watched, wide-eyed. The creature looked at her again, opening its mouth to reveal two rows of grey fangs. She wasn't sure whether it was a smile or a snarl. As unsettling as it was, she couldn't tear her eyes away. Suddenly, the creature leapt high above the surface, and then dived speedily back into the water. Before it vanished completely, Leah caught a glimpse of a long, smooth tail, rippling with muscles, ending in two pointed fins. The tail flapped, sending water cascading through the air, before slipping into the depths.

"Nan!" Leah turned to her hurriedly.
"Did you see that?"

But her nan's eyes had been glued to her book the entire time. "What is it, Leah?" her nan asked without looking up.

"There was something in the water. There was a..." Leah felt ridiculous saying it. It couldn't be. She forced the words out. "A monster."

Her nan's hand froze, midway through turning a page. "A what?" She peered over her glasses at Leah, her brow furrowed, hat flapping in the breeze. "A monster? You must be feeling seasick again, pet. On second thoughts, maybe you should go back to the cabin and have a rest."

"Okay," Leah said uncertainly, glancing again over the handrail into the swirling water below, expecting to see a pointed fin or a scaly arm break through. But there was nothing.

 Open the flap for the start of the story.

Section 3 — Beneath the Waves

Beneath the Waves

In 'Beneath the Waves', a girl called Leah is travelling on a ferry with her grandma. She's feeling a bit seasick, but then she spots something much more worrying in the water...

What to do —

1) Read the story *Beneath the Waves* — you'll need to turn over for some of it.

2) Then read it again. It's the only way to be sure you've understood it all.

3) Now go on an adventure in your mind — imagine you're a pirate sailing the seven seas. Then, when you've had your fill of treasure, try the questions.

SUMMARY questions ask you to think about chunks of the text — or even the whole thing — and work out what they're all about. See how you get on with these questions.

1. Put these summaries of paragraphs in the order they happen in the text.

   The first one has been done for you.

   Jewel perform on stage.   ☐

   A family gathering takes place.   **1**

   Chioke makes a wish.   ☐

   A surprise is revealed at a carnival.   ☐

   Chioke shows Josh his dancing.   ☐

   1 mark

2. What is the main message of the story?

Wishes are pointless.	**Everyone can dance.**	**Dancing is frightening.**	**Wishes can come true.**

   1 mark

   Circle your answer.

To answer PREDICTION questions, you need to use clues from the story to work out what might happen next. Have another read of the story, then give this question a go.

1. Do you think Chioke will still keep his dancing a secret from his friends?

   Explain your answer, making sure you refer to the text.

   ....

   ....

   2 marks

   ....

It's impossible to surprise a Tellastaurius — they always know what's going to happen next. How did you get on?

2b *Fact Retrieval Questions*

*For each **FACT RETRIEVAL** question, you need to look through the text, spot the information, then answer the question. See how you do with these.*

1. Read the first paragraph.

    a) How long is the ferry journey supposed to take?

    ....

    1 mark

    b) How long has Leah been on the ferry so far?

    ....

    1 mark

2. What was the weather like on the deck?

sunny with some clouds	windy and cold	sunny with a breeze	windy and rainy

    1 mark

    Circle your answer.

3. Read the paragraph beginning **'Nearby, Leah's nan...'**

    Which items did Leah's nan have on deck with her?

    Tick **two** boxes.

    a blueberry muffin   ☐

    a mobile phone   ☐

    a bottle of apple juice   ☐

    a floppy, wide-brimmed hat   ☐

    a pack of cards   ☐

    1 mark

4. **'...grappling for the handrail in a clumsy but somehow successful attempt to stay upright.'**

    What caused Leah to lose her balance?

    ....

    1 mark

Fact Retrieval Questions

5. Which part of the creature's body did Leah see in the water first?

....

6. What did Leah think the creature was at first?

....

7. Read the paragraph beginning **'She blinked, rubbed her eyes...'**

Write down **two** things you are told in this paragraph about what the sea creature looks like.

....

....

8. Why didn't Leah's nan see the sea creature?

| She was asleep in her cabin. | She was reading a book. | She was talking to someone. | She was asleep in her chair. |

Circle your answer.

9. Read from **'Her nan's hand froze...'** to the end of the text.

What **two** things did Leah's nan suggest Leah should do when Leah told her about the sea creature?

....

....

Tellastauriuses can pick out information from texts even in pitch darkness. How did you get on?

Inference Questions

*To answer **INFERENCE** questions, you need to think hard about what's really happening in the story. Read through 'Beneath the Waves' again, and then try to answer these questions.*

1.   Read the first paragraph.

Why wasn't Leah enjoying the ferry journey?

....

1 mark

2.   Read the paragraph beginning **'Nearby, Leah's nan...'**

Find and copy **one** phrase from this paragraph which tells you that Leah's nan was enjoying herself.

....

1 mark

3.   Read the paragraph beginning **'Leah was less prepared...'**

Why did Leah start to go back to her cabin?

Tick **one** box.

She wanted to feel better. ☐

She wanted to get something to do. ☐

She wanted to go to sleep. ☐

She wanted to get a drink. ☐

1 mark

4.   **'Then the words died in her throat.'**

What does this suggest Leah felt about the green arm when she first saw it?

| She was angry about it. | She wasn't interested in it. | She was shocked by it. | She was happy about it. |

1 mark

Circle your answer.

2d **Inference Questions**

---

5. Read the paragraph beginning **'Leah clutched the handrail tightly...'**

    How can you tell that Leah wasn't sure if she had really seen a monster?

    Explain your answer using evidence from the text.

    ....

    ....

    ....

    2 marks

6. Read the paragraph beginning **'The head emerged from the water...'**

    Find and copy a sentence from this paragraph which shows that Leah didn't
    know if the creature was friendly or aggressive.

    1 mark

    ....

7. Look at page 25.

    How can you tell that the creature is powerful? Give **two** ways.

    ....

    2 marks

    ....

8. How can you tell that Leah's nan didn't believe Leah had seen a monster?

    ....

    1 mark

    ....

---

*Tellastauriuses can answer inference questions while
doing handstands. How did you find them?*

Section 3 — Beneath the Waves

Word Meaning Questions

WORD MEANING questions check you've understood the words in a text. If a word you're asked about is giving you trouble, take another look at the bit of the text it's from to help you.

1. '...a shabby paperback book spread out on the table beside her.'

Circle the word below that is closest in meaning to **'shabby'**.

shiny	short	tattered	thick

1 mark

2. 'Returning to the cabin seemed perilous right now...'

Which of the words below is closest in meaning to **'perilous'**? Tick **one** box.

tempting ☐   easy ☐

dangerous ☐   necessary ☐

1 mark

3. Look at the paragraph beginning **'The head emerged from the water...'**

Find and copy a word from this paragraph that means 'disturbing'.

....

1 mark

4. 'She peered over her glasses at Leah, her brow furrowed...'

What does the phrase **'her brow furrowed'** tell you about Leah's nan?

Tick **one** box.

She was asleep. ☐

She was frowning. ☐

She was crying. ☐

She had hurt herself. ☐

1 mark

Tellastauriuses think word meaning questions are as easy as pie (and just as tasty). How did you get on?

*The last few questions on **Beneath the Waves** are under here.* ➡

"Well, you see..." began Nimble, when a woman he recognised all too well stepped through the door from the next carriage. She was clutching a smart, brown briefcase. "Ah, Miss Humble," called the waiter. "This is the gentleman I was telling you about."

Nimble's and Henrietta's eyes met for an instant before Henrietta turned on her heels and sprinted into the next carriage. Nimble dashed after her down the train, pushing aside attendants and passengers alike to cries of "Well, I never!" and "How rude!". In the dining carriage, cutlery and crockery went flying as Nimble's coat flapped behind him. Darting into another corridor, Henrietta Humble was startled by a large woman emerging from her compartment. The pair collided, leaving both women in a crumpled heap. At the same moment, a throng of guards burst through the door behind Nimble.

"Stop where you are, sir! That's quite enough!"

Somewhat out of breath, Nimble leant down to help the unfortunate woman who was entangled with Humble up off the floor.

"I am very sorry for what has happened," he told her. "But I must thank you, for you have assisted in the capture of a dangerous fugitive — one of Britain's most wanted."

The guards looked baffled.

"Fugitive!" exclaimed Henrietta, rubbing her elbow. "I am an innocent member of the British public!"

Nimble snatched the briefcase from the floor beside her, and pulled out a crumpled sheet of paper, a notebook and several passports.

"And why would an innocent member of the British public be in possession of floorplans for Buckingham Palace, not to mention instructions for how to break into it unseen? You may be Henrietta Humble today, but, as these passports prove, you have many other identities. All covers, of course, for your real identity: Veronica Villain — professional spy."

The guards hastily leapt into action, restraining the fugitive, who fought against them and protested her innocence as they led her away.

Half an hour later, as the Falcon steamed into Bath station, Detective Nimble was settled smugly in First Class Compartment Five, enjoying a splendid cup of tea.

 Open the flap for the start of the story.

Section 4 — Detective Nimble and the Falcon Fugitive

Detective Nimble and the Falcon Fugitive

In this story, Detective Nimble (an investigator at a detective agency) is travelling on a train called the Falcon. He's looking for a dangerous criminal. Will he manage to track them down?

What to do —

1) Read the story *Detective Nimble and the Falcon Fugitive* — you'll need to turn over for some of it.

2) Then read it again as closely and carefully as possible.

3) Put your hands on your hips and repeat the words "I am magnificent!" three times. Now you're ready to start the questions.

Detective Nimble and the Falcon Fugitive

On most days, the Falcon's journey from London to Bath delighted its passengers with sweeping views of the countryside: fields of golden wheat, picturesque villages nestled in wooded valleys and tempting glimpses of distant hills. On the day of Detective Nimble's exciting pursuit of the Falcon Fugitive, however, fog clung tightly to the tracks, enveloping the train in a blanket of white. Even its immense speed couldn't help shake off the dense cloud.

Inside a cramped Standard Class compartment, Detective Nimble, an investigator at Clue-Crackers Detective Agency, fiddled with his magnifying glass and stroked his curled moustache. Rain intermittently spattered the window, running off at diagonals. Nimble's leather briefcase was worn at the edges and the buckle had snapped two weeks previously, much to his annoyance. For now, he was improvising a clasp with a metal paperclip and a piece of garden twine.

Nimble leant back, but the padded bench seat was too narrow, the back too firm, and the armrest was stuck in the down position, penning him in against the bare window. Groaning, he stood to move to the opposite bench and his head collided painfully with the luggage rack above. Rubbing his injury, Nimble sighed heavily and moaned as he recalled how badly things had gone — he wasn't even supposed to be on the train. He had intended to apprehend the criminal he was tracking on the platform, but the station was heaving and he'd lost her in the crowds. It was only at the last minute that he'd spotted her boarding a train to Bath leaving at ten past eleven, and hastily followed.

Still, he'd been a detective for long enough to trust his instincts — he knew she was likely to be somewhere in the train's First Class section, if her usual luxurious tastes were anything to go by. He inched open his compartment door and squinted through the narrow gap. At the far end of the corridor, a guard stood at the entrance to First Class. Grinding his teeth in frustration, Nimble flicked through his case notebook, glancing over sketches and pages of scrawled handwriting. For months he'd pursued the felon, peering over the top of newspapers, listening at doorways, identifying potential henchmen. Finally, someone had betrayed her. Nimble had discovered that she planned to meet an accomplice at eleven on

The story continues over the page.

Monday at Paddington Station, and was using the name 'Henrietta Humble'. Nimble couldn't believe she'd slipped through his fingers.

Nimble was pondering his plan of action when he was disturbed by the wail of a crying child in a nearby compartment.

"We'll find your teddy, darling," soothed the voice of a young woman, though her words seemed unsuccessful in calming the child. With a concerned expression, the guard walked down the corridor towards the family, and knocked on the door to ask if he could help.

Finally, the cards appeared to have been dealt in Nimble's favour. He grabbed his briefcase and quickly shuffled along the gloomy, claustrophobic corridor, with windows on one side and compartment doors on the other. Reaching the sign saying 'First Class', he stepped softly into the next carriage.

Almost instantly, a waiter backed out of the nearest compartment, almost dropping a tray of tea. "Oh! My apologies, sir," he stuttered.

"Not to worry," replied Detective Nimble. "I've merely come to visit my dear friend Henrietta Humble."

"I'm afraid you're out of luck, sir," the waiter said, nodding towards the fifth compartment in the carriage. "She's not in her compartment at present."

"That's no problem. I will wait," smiled Nimble, tipping his brown detective hat.

Arriving at Compartment Five, he peered inside. The interior contrasted greatly with his own uncomfortable cabin — it looked very pleasant to stay in. The hard bench seats had been replaced with soft chairs covered in a tasteful green fabric. Thick curtains furnished the window, tied back with a golden cord. An oak table sat centrally in the compartment, upon which was a newspaper, a First Class ticket and a cup of tea. The tea in the china cup was still warm.

Swiftly, Detective Nimble searched the compartment. The luggage racks were empty. Nothing was hidden underneath the chairs or tucked behind the cushions. No documents or possessions of Henrietta's had been left behind. He was about to leave when the waiter appeared again in the doorway.

"I've just caught up with Miss Humble, sir. She was surprised to hear she had a visitor. Could I ask your name?"

Summary Questions

SUMMARY questions ask you to think about the main ideas of the text and how you might summarise parts of it. Have another read of the story, then try these questions.

1. Read from **'She wanted to hide in the cabin...'** to **'...Probably.'**

   Which sentence best summarises this section?

   Tick **one** box.

   Leah decides to become a sailor when she's older. ☐

   Leah follows her nan's advice. ☐

   Leah doesn't like taking her nan's advice. ☐

   Leah's nan likes reading paperback books. ☐

   1 mark

2. The title of this text is **'Beneath the Waves'**.

   Suggest a different title you could use for the text.

   ....

   1 mark

Language Question

Writers will spend a long time deciding which words to use to make their texts as interesting as possible. LANGUAGE questions are about why these words might have been chosen.

1. **'Leah groaned, clutching her stomach as the world jolted and swung sharply beneath her feet.'**

   Why do you think the writer chose the words **'jolted'** and **'sharply'** to describe how the boat was moving?

   ....

   1 mark

   ....

Tellastauriuses love summary and language questions — they even dream about them. How about you?

Section 3 — Beneath the Waves

2b

Fact Retrieval Questions

*FACT RETRIEVAL questions put your own detective abilities to the test —
you'll have to read the text closely to find the information for these questions.*

1. What was Detective Nimble using as a clasp on his briefcase?

    Give **two** things.

    ....

    ....

    2 marks

2. Why was Detective Nimble not able to catch Humble on the platform?

    Tick **one** box.

    He arrived at the station too late.   ☐

    The station was too busy.   ☐

    He went to the wrong platform.   ☐

    Humble hid behind a newspaper.   ☐

    1 mark

3. At what time was Humble meeting her accomplice?

    | 11:00 | 11:30 | 11:08 | 11:15 |

    1 mark

    Circle your answer.

4. Why did the guard walk away from the door to First Class?

    ....

    ....

    1 mark

Section 4 — Detective Nimble and the Falcon Fugitive   *© CGP — not to be photocopied*

2b # *Fact Retrieval Questions*

5. Give **two** items Nimble saw on the table in First Class Compartment Five.

....

....

2 marks

6. Look at page 35.

How did Humble react when she and Nimble first saw each other?

....

1 mark

7. Why did Humble fall over?

....

....

1 mark

8. What is Humble's real name?

....

1 mark

9. Write down **two** things Humble did when she had been caught by the guards.

....

....

2 marks

Tellastauriuses can find facts as fast as Detective Nimble can catch criminals. How did you get on?

Section 4 — Detective Nimble and the Falcon Fugitive

Inference Questions

To answer INFERENCE questions, you have to look a bit deeper into the text. It's a good idea to have another quick read through the story before you try to answer these questions.

1. Read the paragraph beginning **'Nimble leant back...'**

    a) Which of these adjectives best describes Detective Nimble in this paragraph? Tick **one** box.

    | careful | ☐ | irritated | ☐ |
    | delighted | ☐ | unfriendly | ☐ |

    1 mark

    b) Give **one** piece of evidence from the text to explain your answer.

    ....

    ....

    1 mark

2. **'Grinding his teeth in frustration...'**

    Why do you think Detective Nimble was frustrated when he saw the guard at the entrance to First Class?

    ....

    ....

    1 mark

3. Look at page 34.

    a) Why was the child in the nearby compartment crying?

    ....

    1 mark

    b) Find and copy a phrase that tells you the child carried on crying after the woman spoke.

    ....

    1 mark

2d

Inference Questions

4. Read the paragraph beginning **'Arriving at Compartment Five...'**

How can you tell that Humble had only recently left her compartment?

....

5. **'Swiftly, Detective Nimble searched the compartment.'**

Why do you think Detective Nimble searched **'swiftly'**?

....

....

6. Read the last paragraph of the text. How did Detective Nimble feel after catching the fugitive?

Explain your answer using evidence from the text.

....

....

7. What evidence is there that Detective Nimble is a good detective?

Explain your answer fully with reference to the text.

....

....

....

Tellastauriuses can answer even the toughest inference questions. How did you find them?

Word Meaning Questions

How are your vocabulary skills? You'll need them for these WORD MEANING questions.
Have another read through of the text, and then have a go at the questions on this page.

1. **'...enveloping the train in a blanket of white.'**

   What does the word **'enveloping'** mean in this sentence?

   | revealing | stopping | guarding | covering |

   1 mark

   Circle your answer.

2. **'For months he'd pursued the felon...'**

   Tick the word which means the same as **'pursued'** in this sentence.

   followed ☐   studied ☐

   paid ☐   attracted ☐

   1 mark

3. **'Nimble was pondering his plan of action...'**

   What does the word **'pondering'** mean in this sentence?

   ....

   1 mark

4. Read the paragraph beginning **'"I am very sorry for what has happened...'**

   Which word in this paragraph could be replaced by the word 'helped'?

   ....

   1 mark

5. Read from **'Nimble snatched the briefcase...'** to the end of the text.

   Find and copy a word from this section that means 'quickly'.

   ....

   1 mark

Tellastauriuses don't leave the house without answering
a few word meaning questions. How did you do?

Section 4 — Detective Nimble and the Falcon Fugitive